TO ELLIOTT & COOPER...

EARL IS A REAL DOG WHO LIVED NEAR US AT THE WISCONSIN HOUSE. His OWNER, LINDA, OWNED A FLOWER NURSERY WHERE WE BOUGHT ALL THE FLOWERS THAT WE PLANTED AROUND THE HOUSE. EARL WANDERED FREELY AROUND THE NURSERY. SUCH A GOOD BOY. WE THOUGHT YOU'D ENJOY READING ABOUT EARL.

Love You Lots .. Mimi & Papa

MERRY CHRISTMAS - 2020

This book is dedicated to a Bulldog who is so much more than just a dog.

Santa Paws

First Printing, 2020
lindadegner@gmail.com
Photography by Linda Degner

Hello,
Earl here,

I have a
secret to
share...

**Santa visited on Christmas Eve night.**
**There I was tangled in more than one light.**

**Santa laughed, "You are a good boy.**
**Please help me spread some Christmas joy."**

"I am just
a bulldog what
can I do?

I have four legs,
don't fly or look
like you."

Santa smiled,
"Let's find what
fits.

This job has
many itsy bits."

"Maybe an Angel with wings glowing white,
keeping us safe as we fly through the night."

"With pine
cones and
ribbons
snuggled in
green,

a circle of
love for
the holiday
scene."

"Scissors and glue help make ornaments to share,

just a little something to show that you care."

"The wigs and hats make me laugh in my belly,
your humor is sweeter than strawberry jelly."

"I want to do more." I said with a smile.
"Whatever you need I am yours for a while."

"What Santa wants the most is a good elf.

One that works hard and won't sit on the shelf."

"I'm in!" I cried as I hopped in my sleigh.
"Giddy up Rudolf. Up, up and away!"

Laughing loudly I heard Santa say,
"You have a red nosed horse pulling your sleigh!"

"Playing piano
with keys black
and white,

I can make music
all through the
night!"

Santa smiled
and then
with a grin,

In his eyes I saw
an idea begin.

"Earl," said Santa, "What if you could be me?
A Santa dressed dog would be something to see!"

**Visions of Santa swirled in my mind,
there must be another dog
that Santa could find.**

"Oh Earl," said Santa, "I believe in you.
I have seen the wonderful things you do."

"This cool Santa suit is where we will start."

"Hmmm, we won't put cool Santa in the cart."

"A goofy hat
and shaded
glasses too?

No,
a cool
looking
Santa
just won't do!"

"A Santa hat must be worn like a crown.
You need more," Santa said with a frown.

"I will add my favorite glasses too,
that way I will look different from you."

"No, I want you to look just like Santa Claus.
Yes!" He exclaimed." You will be my
**Santa Paws!"**

# The End

## Earl here...

I was born October 16, 2014 in northern Wisconsin.
I found my forever home at Christmas that year.
As a half American and half English bulldog puppy I was just like all puppies in that I loved to eat, sleep and play. I grew up in a flower business and found that I loved people, all kinds of people, every person that walked into our business had come to see me!

One day as I was assisting with recycling boxes my human placed a hat on my head. Everyone looked at me and they were so happy, laughing and giggling telling me what a good boy I was. From that moment on I vowed to spread cheer.

This book is my way of spreading smiles across the miles. The pictures are all me.
My human is very clever and considerate making sure that I am extremely comfortable during our photo shoots AND she gives me the best homemade treats when we are done.

Have I told you how much I love treats! Yes, treats are the best. I really like peanut butter, beef, pork, chicken, apples, blueberries, carrots or whatever you are eating.
I love yummy treats!

CPSIA information can be obtained
at www.ICGtesting.com
Printed in the USA
LVHW070407111220
673843LV00002B/14

9 781736 163009